THE LITTLE BOOK OF GEMSTONES

B

By Steve Bennett

INTRODUCTION

Welcome to the world of Mother Nature's treasures: a world full of colourful locations, colourful people, colourful stories and, of course - colourful gems.

This series has been written in an A to Z encyclopaedic format, so that you can dip in and out at your leisure. Whenever you come across a new gemstone or hear someone mention a jewellery term that you have not heard before, you can easily use these books to quickly find out more.

Steve Bennett

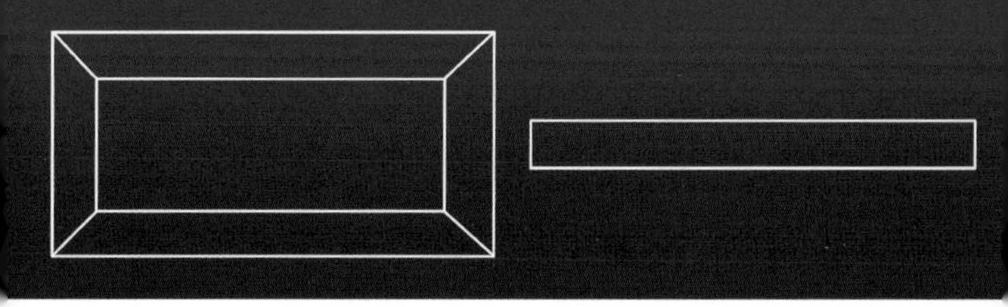

Baguette Cut A thin, long gemstone normally cut with just 14 or 18 facets.

Any gem that is cut into a shape that is thin and long, with parallel facets is regarded as a baguette (or rectangle) cut. Normally a baguette cut would be a step cut and not a brilliant cut gem.

The word comes from the French word for stick or rod; this is why French bread is known as a baguette.

The cut is often used on gems where their crystal structure is naturally oblong. When set at right angles to the band of metal in a solitaire ring it can help elongate the look of the finger.

The cut is increasing in popularity for channel set Diamond rings, where baguette cut gems are tightly set parallel to each other.

Baguette cuts, with their minimal number of facets, do not return much brilliance or fire. The cut looks extremely modern and is wonderful at highlighting clarity and depth of colour: an ideal cut for vividly coloured gemstones. If you are buying a piece of jewellery with baguette cut diamonds it is important to purchase a slightly higher clarity grade than you might normally. This is because the baguette shape is very open and does not have facets on its table; the lapidarist cannot hide inclusions as they would in a round brilliant cut. A tapered baguette is one where the gem is cut thinner at one end.

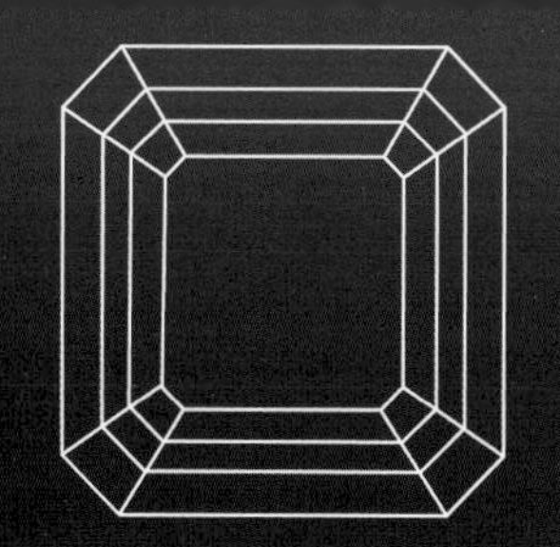

Barion Cut A cut developed in the 1970s that features unique facets shaped like a quarter moon.

First of all the Barion cut is really more of a family of cuts than an individual cut.

It was one of the first 'mixed cuts' which shares aspects of a brillian and step cut. Imagine a brilliant cu gemstone constructed with triangula and kite shaped facets then add facet directly below the crown that look lik the shape of a quarter moon.

The Barion cut can be applied to rounds, trilliants, ovals: almost any shape where you can create a brilliant cut. To-date over 90 Barion Cuts have been documented.

The Barion cut was invented in 1970 in Johannesburg, South Africa by a lapidarist named Basil Watermeyer. He named the cut by merging the start of his Christian name with the end of his wife's, Marion. Luckily, 'Barion' was never registered as a trademark and lapidarists are encouraged to use the cut.

The cut is very difficult to perform. If you don't get it absolutely symmetrical, the moon-shaped facets can end up looking like a choppy sea! Done properly, the perceived colour of the gem will often be increased and at the same time the yield will normally be higher than a gem of the same size cut more traditionally.

Baroque The word originates from Portuguese and is usually used to describe Pearls with an irregular shape. However, Pearls don't have exclusive rights on the word: it is also used in music to describe pieces that are elaborate.

Most Freshwater Pearls are baroque and perfectly round ones are extremely rare.

Freshwater Cultured Pearls tend to be more spherical, as the foreign body injected into the shell (which is used as the catalyst for the Pearl growing process) is normally a perfectly rounded sphere.

Whilst it is true that baroque Pearls are generally less expensive than round Pearls, they often have a wonderful play of colour. This is not caused by multiple layers within the nacre causing light to be refracted at different angles as it is with round Pearls, but due to light being bounced off the irregular shaped surface in different directions, colliding together to form a cocktail of hues.

When a baroque shape is more baguette-like, it is often renamed Biwa Pearl. Rarely set into rings, baroque Pearls are used in modern, bracelets and necklaces.

Bastnäsite An incredibly rare gemstone that glows a cognac orangey colour.

A close friend Shawn, a gem hunter, born in Pakistan, he travelled to his home country in search of gem rough. His quest took him into the remote Zagi Mountains where he came across miners hunting a gem known as Bastnäsite.

This gemstone, which looks similar in appearance to a translucent Smokey Quartz, was first unearthed in Sweden in the early 1800s and was named after the Bastnäs Mine where it was discovered.

Although not a rare mineral (Bastnäsite can be found in America, Africa, China and Mongolia), 'gem quality' material is virtually unheard of. So far we have only acquired several pieces, however Shawn is planning another trip, and we hope to be able to discover more pieces in the future.

Also spelt 'Bastnaesite', the gem is very unusual in that it contains a large percentage of the element cerium. One of the latest discoveries is said to be Ambatofinandrahana in Madagascar; however we have yet to see them ourselves. For now the only deposit we are sourcing from is the Kunar Province in Afghanistan.

Beads Since antiquity, gemstone beads have been set in jewellery.

When mining for gems, it is common to find a mixture of qualities. While the best gems are set into rings, pendants and earrings, others that are not to the same exacting standards are often faceted into a bead shape, and drilled by hand to make bracelets and necklaces.

Other types of beads often used in costume jewellery can include glass, plastic, stones, ceramics and wood. Although discoveries in burial sites have shown that beads were used in jewellery thousands of years ago, we are unsure whether this early form of jewellery was for personal adornment or simply used as talismans. Today with an increasing amount of people making their own jewellery at home, there has been a significant increase in the quality of gemstone beads. No longer are beads just a bi-product from cutting faceted gems, they now have an entire category of cuts and shapes of their own. From smaller sea beads to side drilled cubes, from flat pear shapes to side drilled twisted hearts, the list goes on and on. Most opaque beaded gemstones are cut by machines in China, whilst the majority of transparent beads are hand cut in India.

Beauty Of all items known to man, gemstones represent the most everlasting beauty of all.

For any mineral to be regarded as a gem, anyone in the gem industry will tell you that it must be durable, rare and, above all, beautiful. As "beauty is in the eye of the beholder" and as we all have a different perception of what is beautiful, it is certainly the most difficult of the three requirements to define. In a Diamond, beauty is often measured by its clarity: the clearer it is, the more valuable it is. Coloured gemstones on the other hand, primarily have their beauty judged by the vividness of their colour.

When we see beauty it awakens our feel-good senses. Beauty can be observed in many things including culture, nature, the opposite sex, clothes, jewellery and, of course, gemstones. What makes gemstones more glamorous than almost any other item on Earth is the rareness of their beauty. Only when a multitude of necessary chemical elements, the right environment, the correct pressure and the right temperature are combined together - and all for the required period - is Mother Nature able to create such beautifully colourful, natural and rare treasures.

Whilst beautiful flowers will eventually die, beautiful pictures eventually fade and beautiful memories become distorted, the beauty you see in a gemstone today (as long as it is properly cared for) should last thousands of years. Many generations from now, the person that is holding your gorgeous Emerald ring, should be viewing a ring that's just as beautiful in appearance to them as it is to you. For me, gemstones offer the longest lasting form of beauty that can be possessed by man.

When we think of an object as beautiful it normally means that we are attracted to its colour, shape, style and design. But beauty in gemstones often goes deeper. The beauty derived from

knowing the mystery, magic, folklore, legends and history surrounding coloured gemstones is unrivalled by any other purchasable item.

One final thought: the beauty experienced in a place, person or object often makes us feel happiness and warmth, and this feeling is amplified by our memories and past experiences. Let me give you two examples. Firstly, I find my personal gem collection grows more and more beautiful as I gain a stronger and stronger understanding about the gems. The more I research them, the better I know the myths and legends surrounding them, the more beautiful they somehow appear to me. Secondly, I believe that pieces of jewellery that have been received as a gift on special occasions and anniversaries, plus those that have been passed on from previous generations, have an additional inherent beauty.

Belmont The largest open pit mine in Brazil.

Although there are a few states in Brazil where artisanal Emerald mining is still in full swing, there is one mine operating in the Cinturao Esmeraldífero ('Emerald belt') of Minas Gerais that is at the cutting edge of mining technology. This story is set in Itabira and begins in the late 1930s when a young entrepreneur farmer, Mauro Ribeiro, started to transport diesel from Belo Horizonte (the capital city of Minais Gerias)to the local iron mines. He pushed his business hard and within just a few years had many diesel trucks travelling the route every

Owner Marcelo and Steve Bennett at the Belmont Mine .

day. He then opened his own iron mine and eventually was so successful that the authorities forcefully took over the concern and Mauro went back to farming. On his land a new railway track was built to transport the extracted minerals from the mines and many years later in 1977, whilst switching the points on the track, a young train driver spotted a green gemstone lying on the ground.

The worker took the gem to Mauro and suggested that he allowed him to take it to a nearby town where he knew gemstones were often traded. Mauro agreed and when the railroad worker returned, they shared the profits.

As Mauro already had a wealth of mining experience, it wasn't long before he was granted a licence by the government to start mining for Emeralds. Over the years the mine has had periods of strong production followed by long periods of minimal production. I met with the mine's owner Marcelo Ribeiro (Mauro's grandson) and he kindly gave us an in-depth tour of his facility.

The open pit mine is incredibly vast and is the second largest I have seen (the only one bigger is Gemfields Emerald Mine in Zambia). The top soils are a vibrant red colour formed from the Baltic rocks below. The pit is now some 300 to 400 feet deep. JCBs work at the rock face and when they hit a layer where their geologists believe there is potential of Emeralds being discovered, they scoop up all of the soil and rocks into the back of a gigantic dumper truck and the extracted minerals are taken to the sorting facility, where hopefully a green treasure or two will be found.

Marcelo explained that currently for every full dumper truck, which holds over 20 tonnes, they extract approximately 5 grams of rough Emerald of which approximately 20% is of gem quality. That's a lot of work for very few grams, especially when

Steve examining a huge rough Emerald at the Belmont mine.

you consider how many thousands of tonnes of earth have already been excavated just to reach the pay dirt (pay dirt is a phrase used by miners to describe the reaching of a gem rich pocket or layer).

When you get to a certain depth in an open pit mine, if the gem rich vein continues to dip lower into the earth, there comes a point when it's no longer possible to dig any deeper. You will notice in photographs how these types of mines have big steps rising to the surface. The reason for this is that the rock faces would be unstable and liable to collapsing if they were cut vertically Therefore if at the bottom of the mine you want to dig 10 metres deeper, you need to push back and excavate soil and rocks at every level from the top of the mine to the bottom. If you want to go deeper at the bottom of the mine, it can take as long as a year to push back each level allowing the bottom area to eventually be mined.

With so much cost involved in labour and fuel, in 2005 Marcelo decided to extend the Belmont Mine underground. Today they still operate the open pit mine, but a lot of attention and effort has gone into building a vast network of tunnels and shafts as they chase Emeralds further and further into the Earth's crust.

This step feature prevents the rock collapsing under its own weight as digging progressively gets deeper below the surface.

Before we put on our helmets and went underground to see the operation, Marcelo paused to tell me a story: In the late 1980s, his grandfather hit a pocket of Emerald that produced many grams of weight. Everyday more and more Emeralds were coming out of the ground. For a while he had more gemstones than he had customers. So he instructed the mine's manager to take all of the scree (waste from the mine) and rough rocks that they had excavated which were rich in Emeralds and to secretly cover them in earth. He was concerned that if he continued to mine so much and stored the gems that they would get stolen (theft and security is a real concern for gemstone

mines all over the world). After the rich ore was covered, he instructed the miners to work on another area in the mine. Only later in a period of low yields did they return to the area where they had had a great success.

For many years the hidden rich scree and ore remained a secret of the grandfather and the mine manager. A few years ago after a period of lack-lustre performance Marcelo confided in the mine manager that he was concerned whether the mine was still viable and that if he didn't hit a good vein soon they may have to close. The mine manager, now in his late sixties, took Marcelo to one side and told him the story about his grandfather's great find and led Marcelo to where the mound of highly gem rich rock was buried.

Today Marcelo does not rely on luck in mining but uses the very latest technology in prospecting for gems. Whilst his open pit mine is the second largest I have seen, his underground mine is the most impressive I have ever had the pleasure of entering. At four metres high and five metres wide, big articulated trucks can travel through its three kilometres of tunnels.

During my visit fifteen miners and security guards were currently working the underground mine. The tunnel

descends 40 metres from the height at the mine entrance and at various points the tunnel splits and weaves in several directions as miners chase an area known as the "reaction zone". The reaction zone is located alongside volcanic pegmatites that have been pushed up through cracks and crevices in the earth. The pegmatites are rich in beryllium, the building block for members of the Beryl family such as Emeralds, Aquamarine and Morganite. As the pegmatite cooled along its edge it picked up trace elements from the surrounding rocks and structures, in this area the rocks often had traces of chromium, which is the second building block needed for the formation of Emeralds. But that's just the foundations, for an Emerald crystal to grow it has to be exposed to the correct temperature for the right period of time; it then has to cool at a particular rate, all of this happening at the correct pressure. Of course if it wasn't this difficult, if it did not need the coming together of many elements all at the right time, then there would be gemstones aplenty. But then they wouldn't be rare and they would possess no inherent value: in fact there would then be very little separating them from manmade crystals.

Not only does Marcelo employ the latest technology in both prospecting

for Emeralds and then extracting them, he uses an incredibly advanced process to sort and identify the gems. When miners are working at the rock face often they will see with their own eyes larger pieces of rough gemstones. However, identifying smaller pieces amongst tonnes of excavated rough is sometimes like looking for a needle in a haystack. In fact it's worse! At least if you are looking for a needle you have lost in a haystack, you have the encouragement of knowing it is there somewhere. When you are sifting through tonnes of rocks, pebbles and dirt in the vain hope that you might find a precious gemstone, the task becomes very difficult. Marcelo a few years ago decided to look for a solution that was less labour intensive and one that retrieved a higher percentage of the Emeralds sporadically hidden in the rough. Traditionally miners would put the excavated material in a wire mesh pan and then swirl it around in a river to wash it and hopefully they would find a gem or two. This technique is similar to the way you may have seen images in Wild West movies where they were panning for gold. Next came big industrial washing machines that then spit out the clean rough rocks on to a conveyor belt, at which either side stood a team of eagle eyed gem sorters. But Marcelo wanted to revolutionise his operation and had heard about a

technology that was used in the coffee bean industry for automatically sorting good beans from bad.

This technology is breathtaking. First the rough rocks are washed and tumbled and any obvious pieces of Emerald are removed. Next the clean rocks are spread out on a high speed conveyor belt at the end of which is a three foot drop. As the stones free-fall over the end, a set of digital cameras film them and

instantly analyse their colour. If the computer spots any pieces are green it fires a series of air jets at the stone altering the direction of its fall, and blows the potential gem into a separate container. It is incredible to watch and what is even more impressive is that it has an accuracy higher than that of human gem sorters.

When it comes to the environment, Belmont take their corporate responsibilities very seriously. Rather than just pump their waste water back into the river, which is what unfortunately happens in some areas, they have designed a series of man-made filtration lakes. As each one steps down the hillside you can physically see the muddy water getting cleaner and cleaner and by the time it is pumped into the river it's good enough to drink!

I really enjoyed my time at the Belmont Mine in Itabira and would like to thank Marcelo for giving so much time to explain how his mine operated. Whilst I am a huge supporter of small artisanal miners, it is also important to appreciate the impact larger companies such as Belmont have in terms of growing the market for the wonderful coloured treasures that we all love to collect.

Benitoite One of the most fascinating and rarest gems yet discovered.

Imagine the colour of a light blue Sapphire, the fire of a Diamond and the rarity of winning the lottery 10 times in a row! That's Benitoite! Most pieces faceted in the world to-date weigh less than 0.5ct, are Swiss blue in appearance and have a slightly cloudy clarity. I managed to acquire one piece, which has incredible clarity and a colour similar to that of the finest Kashmir Sapphire. It also weighs a very impressive 0.75ct. I have shown this piece to several friends in the trade and every one of them has commented that it is probably the finest piece ever faceted!

Discovered by a gentleman named James Couch in 1907 near the San Benito River in California (hence its name), the gem was thought to be a Sapphire. However, after sending several pieces to the University of California, a mineralogist named Dr George Louderback identified them as a brand new mineral. In 1985, as 'gem-quality' Benitoite had still only been discovered in California, it was named California's official state gem. For 102 years this gem has been highly prized by collectors and only a handful of top quality pieces have ever been faceted.

32

Beryl A biblical family of highly respected gemstones.

The Beryl family boasts some of the finest and most historical gems available. When green, it is referred to as Emerald; when red, Bixbite; when blue, Aquamarine; when pink, Morganite; when colourless, Goshenite; and when yellow it is known as Heliodor, or Yellow or Golden Beryl.

The name is derived from the Greek "beryllos", which was used when referring to gems with a precious blue-green colour. In its pure form the gem is colourless, and it is due to different impurities that provide Beryl with its varied offspring.

Worn in jewellery for centuries, references of this gem can be found in the Bible, "the wheels of God's throne are described as having the appearance of gleaming Beryl". (Ezekiel 1:16). The latest addition is pink Beryl, which was discovered by G.F. Kunz in 1911. He named it Morganite after the famous banker J.P. Morgan, who was both a gem collector and one of Tiffany's largest customers.

Bhavyia

Specialist in colour

Bi-Coloured Tourmaline

Bi-Coloured Tourmaline is a miracle of nature. One of the most beautiful gemstones on the planet is the incredibly complex gemstone, Tourmaline. Just one glance at its chemical composition and all but the scientists amongst us will quickly glaze over the formula.

So to find a piece of Tourmaline that makes the transition from one gorgeous colour to another is nothing short of a miracle of nature. But if Nature can do it once, why can't she do it twice?

Why, if Tourmaline can be found in every colour of the rainbow, can't it have several different colour combinations? There is no denying that the transition from bottle green to bubble gum pink witnessed in Bi-Coloured Tourmaline is one of the most beautiful, natural journeys on the planet, but why does it not occur with other Tourmaline colours? To find out the answer to this question I quizzed Brazilian gem expert Joas Salvador.

Joas explained that it's not impossible to find Bi-Coloured Tourmalines that feature other colours, in fact over the years Joao explained that there had been a fair amount that traverse from a brown to green colour, but these had not been coming out of the ground in

Steve buying Bi-Coloured Tourmaline from mine owner Saint-Clair.

recent times. Other combinations such as red to yellow, however, are so rare that they tend to be snapped up by wealthy collectors. Joas told me that many Tourmaline miners in Minas Gerais knew one or two buyers of the incredibly rare colour combinations and normally these pieces would be sold over the phone before anyone else even got to see them.

Some of the finest Bi-colour Tourmaline comes from the Pederneira Mine in Minas Gerais, Brazil. The mine is owned by Saint-Clair Fonseca Júnior and on a recent visit to Brazil he showed me around his mine. I asked him how much Bi-Coloured Tourmaline the mine was currently producing. Saint-Clair explained that the gem was found in small pockets and that once they found a pocket they might have a good yield for a few days, but then they could go months, sometimes years before another lucrative find is discovered. This erratic supply explains why my company went three years without being able to source a single deal for the gem and such is the international demand for Bi-Coloured Tourmaline, that it took a long, drawn out negotiation with Saint-Clair to get him to sell a small parcel that he had recently unearthed.

The gem's crystal structure tends to be

thin and long which results in the gem normally being faceted as a baguette or octagon shape. Because lapidarists will always try and show the maximum shift of colour, the outcome is often a very long gemstone. Most Bi-Coloured Tourmalines are set into pendants, however on the odd occasion a pair of similar pieces are cut, a jeweller will try and set them in long, dangling earrings.

When eye-clean, a Bi-Coloured Tourmaline can sometimes demand over a thousand dollars per carat and even heavily included pieces are often traded at over one hundred and fifty dollars per carat.

The main difference between Bi-Coloured Tourmaline and Watermelon Tourmaline is that the latter tends to have pink in the middle with a surrounding circle of green, hence its name. Whilst Bi-Colour Tourmaline is faceted, Watermelon Tourmaline is normally cut into thin discs.

Other areas where Bi-Coloured Tourmaline is also mined include Nigeria, Madagascar and Afghanistan.

Birefringence Most gemstones are birefringent, however the optical effect is only noticeable to the naked eye in a few.

Also referred to as double refraction, birefringence is the splitting of a single ray of light into two rays.

Double refraction is often beautiful to observe and is best witnessed in Zircon. As the light splits in a faceted gemstone, it hits the inside of the pavilion facets and bounces around like an image in a hall of mirrors. The effect seen when studying a gem that has birefringence through its table and crown facets is incredibly beautiful.

In addition to Zircon, the effect can also be seen in Calcite and Moissanite (a man made item that is sold as a replacement to Diamond).

Birefringent gemstones have two different refractive indices; this makes the optical phenomena very useful for gem dealers to correctly identify certain man-made fakes from real gemstones. In order to measure birefringence, a gem is placed in a refractometer and two readings are taken.

All gemstones that are pleochroic are also birefringent. In fact other than Diamonds, Spinel and members of the Garnet family, most other gemstones featured in this book are all birefringent; however some split the light more than others.

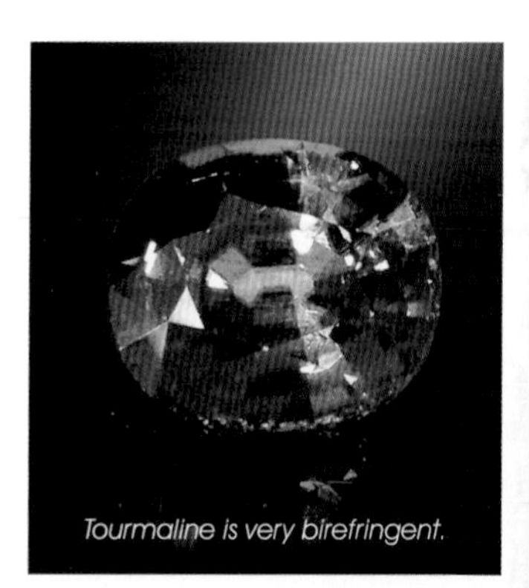

Tourmaline is very birefringent.

recent times. Other combinations such as red to yellow, however, are so rare that they tend to be snapped up by wealthy collectors. Joas told me that many Tourmaline miners in Minas Gerais knew one or two buyers of the incredibly rare colour combinations and normally these pieces would be sold over the phone before anyone else even got to see them.

Some of the finest Bi-colour Tourmaline comes from the Pederneira Mine in Minas Gerais, Brazil. The mine is owned by Saint-Clair Fonseca Júnior and on a recent visit to Brazil he showed me around his mine. I asked him how much Bi-Coloured Tourmaline the mine was currently producing. Saint-Clair explained that the gem was found in small pockets and that once they found a pocket they might have a good yield for a few days, but then they could go months, sometimes years before another lucrative find is discovered. This erratic supply explains why my company went three years without being able to source a single deal for the gem and such is the international demand for Bi-Coloured Tourmaline, that it took a long, drawn out negotiation with Saint-Clair to get him to sell a small parcel that he had recently unearthed.

The gem's crystal structure tends to be

In addition to Zircon, the effect can also be seen in Calcite and Moissanite (a man made item that is sold as a replacement to Diamond).

Birefringent gemstones have two different refractive indices; this makes the optical phenomena very useful for gem dealers to correctly identify certain man-made fakes from real gemstones. In order to measure birefringence, a gem is placed in a refractometer and two readings are taken.

All gemstones that are pleochroic are also birefringent. In fact other than Diamonds, Spinel and members of the Garnet family, most other gemstones featured in this book are all birefringent; however some split the light more than others.

Tourmaline is very birefringent.

Birthstones There are 17 official birthstones. The origin of birthstones is believed to be linked to the breastplate of Aaron. The 1st century historian Josephus (also known as Yosef Ben Matityahu) and St Jerome in the 5th century both wrote about the connection between the breastplate of Aaron and the twelve months of the year. That said, it was not until the

sixteenth century in Poland that the wearing of birthstones for the particular month in which you were born became recognised. Prior to this period it is believed that many people acquired twelve different gems and wore them one by one, changing them on the first day of every month.

Over the centuries, different countries and different religions have made various alterations to the list. George Kunz in his book, "The Curious Lore of Precious Stones", collated various birthstone charts and as it is the most comprehensive list we've found, we have included it on the following page.

In 1912, the American National Jewelers' Association compiled a new birthstone list, replacing many of the historical gemstone names with their current names, and in 1938 The American Gem Society made several further amendments. In 1952, the Jewelry Industry Council of America sponsored the birthstone list which remains until this day (with the exception of Tanzanite, which was only discovered in 1967 and was added to the official birthstone list on the 30th of October 2002).

Nowadays there is no excuse not to invest in birthstones. Historically some of the gemstones were often

unavailable in many countries and others were not suitable for setting. Today, even though Alexandrite and Tanzanite can sometimes be difficult to find, most months now have more than one gem associated with them, leaving us little excuse for not having at least a few pieces of our birthstone in our jewellery box.

Even with the many changes over the centuries, millions of people still believe in the positive power of wearing your correct birthstone as a talisman. Nobody can deny the positive effects felt when wearing the correct birthstone, even if it is purely because of a placebo.

Month	Associated Gemstone
January	Garnet
February	Amethyst
March	Aquamarine
April	Diamond
May	Emerald
June	Pearl, Moonstone or Alexandrite
July	Ruby
August	Peridot
September	Sapphire
October	Opal or Tourmaline
November	Topaz or Citrine
December	Turquoise, Zircon or Tanzanite

Bixbite or Pezzottaite? These two gemstones are often confused.

Also known as Red Emerald and Scarlet Emerald, Bixbite is regarded by many as the rarest member of the Beryl family. The gem is named in honour of the legendary mineralogist Maynard Bixby (1853 – 1935) of Utah, America, who was believed to have first discovered the gem in 1904.

Many gems marketed as Bixbite are in fact a different gem known as Pezzottaite. The confusion arises as both their chemical construction and appearance are almost identical. Bixbite, however, is currently only mined in two locations on the planet: the Wah Wah Mountains in Utah, America, and in the Catron and Sierra Counties, New Mexico. Pezzottaite, on the other hand, was first discovered in Madagascar in 2002. Although the mines are now said to be depleted, luckily there has been a recent discovery in Afghanistan.

Manganese causes the gem's stunning red appearance, and although the gem is often heavily included and at best translucent, many collectors regard the gem as a greater acquisition than Ruby. The most covetable colour is a deep pink. Unfortunately over the past few years, we have not been able to source the gem in any reasonable quantity.

Black Diamond

Black Diamond is highly fashionable, with incredible lustre and unparalleled scintillation. Black Diamonds are a stunning and very fashionable variety of Diamond. Although it lacks dispersion and the internal brilliance of its colourless sister, a quality Black Diamond has the ability to display an intense surface lustre, with an almost metallic shimmer.

Natural Black Diamonds are found predominantly in Africa. As with all Diamonds, they were formed in the earth many millions of years ago and have been pushed to the Earth's surface by volcanic eruptions.

Black Diamonds have becom increasingly popular in recent year Although not strictly black, the contain numerous dark inclusions th give this Diamond its black look. Whe buying Black Diamonds it's best t always assume they have been treate especially if they are a true jet blac colour. As the only optical effect w are looking for in Black Diamonds i lustre and scintillation, a buyer's mai focus should be on the quality of it surface. It is imperative that it has bee well cut and polished that it is free o major defects such as pits, cracks an crevices.

·lack Gems & Associations

. classic colour chosen by jewellery ·earers of all ages.

lack is the ultimate dark colour that conveys legance, although strictly speaking it is not ·uly a colour at all. Black gems, as with any oject that is black, do not reflect any visible ght.

·oloured gemstones obtain their colour ·y the way their atoms absorb and reflect ifferent colours of the spectrum.

· red gem, such as a Ruby, absorbs all of the ;reen and blue colours of the spectrum and ·eflects only the red rays, while colourless ;emstones such as Diamonds and Zircon

reflect all colours of the spectrum. Black gems on the other hand, absorb all colours and therefore none are reflected back to the eye.

In ancient times, when men wore black they were said to have good sense and fortitude, while single women wearing the colour were said to be fickle and foolish (don't shoot the messenger! I'm just quoting ancient history: when women wear black today they are not foolish at all, quite the opposite). When married women wore the colour however, it stood for perseverance and constant love. The colour was also associated with Saturdays and the planet Saturn.

Black is also the colour of rebellion, which could be true in the gem world as there are so few gems that are naturally black; indeed, these could be deemed as nature's rebellions. Only a handful of gems found on Earth are naturally true black: Jet, Haematite and Black Spinel – although the latter is very rare indeed. Black Onyx is actually a Chalcedony, which has been dyed using a technique that is over 2000 years old. The black gem Tektite was created millions of years ago when a meteorite fell to earth and morphed with rocks on the surface of the earth to create one of the few out-of-space gems. Natural Black Diamonds are rarely strictly black, as they nearly

always feature dark inclusions which create an appearance similar to that of a black raven feather with a shimmering black lustre.

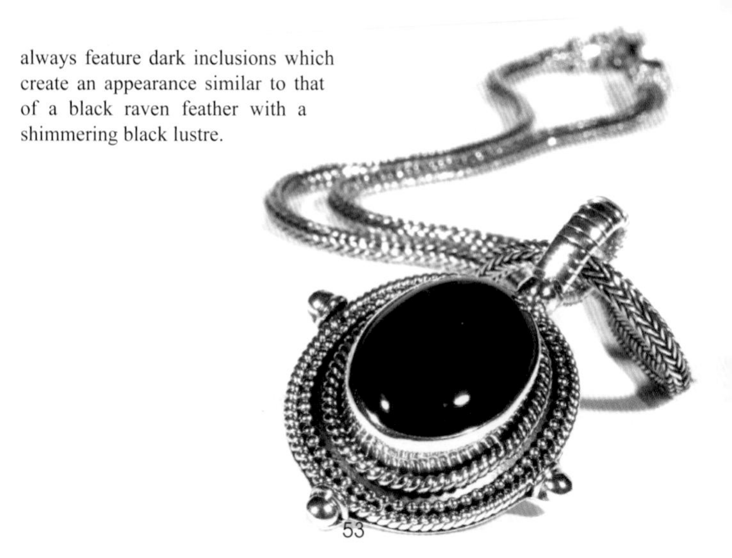

Bleeding The draining of a colour in a gemstone due to lighting conditions is known as bleeding.

This is the best way I can think of describing it: you know how you tend to lose colour when you badly cut yourself? Well, that is what we mean when we say that a gemstone bleeds. If you view a gem under one light source and then under another some gems will suffer the same effect. Bleeding is not be confused with the effect known as "colour change" where a totally different hue is seen, it's more to do with the draining of colour.

For example most Sapphires when worn indoors under incandescent light can often lack sparkle; their tone seems to diminish and the gem almost fades, but taken back outside into sunlight their tone is instantly revitalised.

Two gems that bleed more than most I have seen are Pink Tourmaline and Rubellite. Their colour becomes more brownish under incandescent lighting and they appear to lose a lot of transparency. Although this is not strictly bleeding, it is the nearest gemmological term I could find to describe its change.

Rhodolite Garnet, especially the famed Naktamunda Rhodolite, will appear a muddy colour under candle light or indoor lighting, yet turn on your fluorescent lamp, or hold them to your window and their colour is described by many experts as the finest coloured gemstone on the planet. My good friend Manuj introduced me to it I could not see what all the fuss was about, but he then led me to his office window, and opened the blind, I was amazed at the transformation in the gem; once it had stopped bleeding it was truly stunning.

Bloodstone The official gemstone for the astrological sign of Aries.

Treasured in ancient times, Bloodstone (also known as Heliotrope) served as the birthstone for March, until it was replaced in 1912 by Aquamarine. Once referred to as the martyr's stone, medieval Christians often carved scenes of the crucifixion into Bloodstone.

According to legend, the origin of this gemstone formed when Christ's blood fell to the foot of the cross, staining Jasper below. A fine example of carved Bloodstone can be found in the Louvre featuring a seal of the famous German Emperor, Rudolf II.

The virtues ascribed to this gem are that it is good for circulation of both energy and blood in the body. It is said to aid in the removal of energy blocks, and placing several pieces of this gemstone in the home is suggested to enhance the flow of life's energy.

Gemmologist George Fredick Kunz wrote "Aries. Who on this world of ours his eyes, in Aries open shall be wise, if always on his hand there lies a Bloodstone". Bloodstone is a member of the Chalcedony group of gems.

Blue Diamond

Blue Diamond is said to be the second most expensive substance on earth, only surpassed by natural Red Diamonds!

Natural fancy-coloured Diamonds are amongst the most expensive and valuable of all gemstones. Coloured Diamonds, especially Blue Diamonds, are becoming increasingly popular with collectors and celebrities.

Nothing quite matches a Blue Diamond in colour: being comparable to a crossbreed of the deepest London Blue Topaz and darkest Santa Maria Aquamarine, it really does have a uniqueness all of its own.

Natural Blue Diamonds are exceptionally rare and historically could cost up to 20 times more than White Diamonds of the same clarity and carat weight. Today to obtain their vibrant blue colour, most Blue Diamonds on the market are heat treated and/or irradiated. That said, they still often demand a higher price than a colourless Diamond of an equivalent grade. Without doubt the most famous Blue Diamond of all time is the 45.2ct Hope Diamond.

Blue Gems and Associations are the hottest selling colour of gemstone so far this century.

Reputedly the most popular male colour, blue promotes calmness and tranquillity and is aesthetically perceived as a cool colour. It lowers the heart rate and breathing, and is also believed to suppress appetite.

When a man wears blue he is said to be wise and thoughtful; a lady in blue is said to be polite and vigilant. The colour is associated with Friday and the planet Venus.

When it comes to blue gems there are several to choose from, the most famous being Sapphire. Although today Sapphires have been discovered in many different hues, historically it was believed that the only colour Sapphires could be found in was blue. It is for this reason that when the word Sapphire is used without a colour prefix, it is always assumed to be blue.

Since its discovery in 1967, Tanzanite has now become possibly the most sought after of all blue gemstones.

If you are looking for a light blue gem with great clarity, then March's

birthstone, Aquamarine, might be your preferred choice. Topaz is another gem that is available in blue and is given different prefixes, dependent on its tone. Sky Blue Topaz is the name given to the lighter of the Topaz shades, Swiss Blue refers to medium tones and dark blue is known as London Blue Topaz.

The ultimate collectable of all blue gemstones has to be Benitoite. This gemstone is incredibly rare and has an appearance similar to Tanzanite, but is so rare that it is approximately a million times rarer than Diamond.

Other blue gems include Iolite and Kyanite; sometimes Zircon, Diamond and Spinel can be found in blue. For many years Garnet was said to come in every colour except blue; however, everything changed recently when there was such a discovery in Madagascar.

Not all blue gems however are transparent: Turquoise, Sodalite, and Amazonite are all attractive opaque blue stones. Probably the most collectable opaque blue gem at the moment is known as Larimar.

Blue Moonstone Quartz

Unique, intriguing and so far only found in one deposit.

One of the most intriguing discoveries in Brazil over the past 10 years is the small deposit of Blue Moonstone Quartz in one of the oldest gemstone mines in South Brazil. Some 30 feet underground in a small area known as "The Urugaena", a thin seam of slightly grey Quartz was discovered. 'At first it

didn't look that exciting underground', says the mine owner; 'However when it was brought to the surface it had the appearance like that of a cross between Moonstone and Blue Fire Opal, it's truly a real treasure and a heavenly gemstone.'

My good friends who facet this gemstone for me tell me that to get the very best out of the gemstone and to maximise its mystical Moonstone-like glow, you have to be very patient when studying the rough, being sure to view it from every single angle before making the first cut. Get it right and the gemstone is truly beautiful, get it wrong and it just doesn't have the same gorgeous, almost magical appearance. Blue Moonstone Quartz has so far only been discovered in Brazil and locals believe that the gemstone instils and nurtures love. This is a must have gemstone for all collectors.

Blue Sapphire

Fit for a princess.

Blues are still amongst the most popular and sought after type of Sapphire and have been the prized possessions of emperors, kings, queens and collectors for thousands of years. Of all the coloured gemstones it is possibly the most renowned and demanded. Royalty have been known to give Sapphires over Diamonds as engagement rings because they are known to be far rarer than the latter. The most notable producer of fine Blue Sapphires is Sri Lanka and it is often referred to by its previous name, Ceylon Sapphire.

As Sapphire is renowned for being blue, when the word is used without a colour prefix, it is assumed that one is talking about Blue Sapphire. All other colours are regarded as "fancy Sapphires" and should be prefixed with their colour. Just as in the wine world it is improper to say Chardonnay Chablis, it would be equally wrong to say Blue Sapphire when describing the Blue variety: being politically correct you simply say, Sapphire.

Evaluating Sapphires

The most attractive Sapphires are those that are a pure blue. Whilst pure body colours are desirable in most gemstones, those whose colour is a primary colour such as the red of Rubies and the blue of Sapphire, really can demand a price premium when their hue is pure. That said, some gem collectors prefer their Blue Sapphires to have a 10 to 15% purple mix within the gem's colour.

In terms of saturation you will sometimes see a greyish mask (see mask heading in Volume II to get a better handle on saturation and masks) and if the gem lacks life this could be the cause. In terms of tone it depends on your preference between lighter cornflower blues and deeper royal blues. Unfortunately today we see far too many Sapphires on the market, especially from some locals in China

and Australia, where the tone is almost 100% (i.e. black).

Another important evaluation criterion for both members of the corundum family (Sapphire and Ruby) is whether the gem bleeds or not (see bleeding heading). When some Sapphires are worn indoors under incandescent light, they can often lack sparkle, their tone seems to diminish and the gem almost fades, but take them back outside and they instantly revitalise. Not all Sapphires bleed in the same way and the level of their bleeding depends on their chemical composition. Probably more than any other gem (with the exception maybe of Pearls), Sapphires have often been valued more for their origin than their beauty. But to paraphrase the most legendary of all gem explorers ever, George Kunz, great gemstones can be found in any location and poor ones can be unearthed at locales that are renowned for the most highly prized. You are just as likely to find a poor quality Sapphire in Kashmir as a stunner in China.

The key evaluation criteria for Sapphire, as with all coloured gems, remain the vividness of its colour, its transparency, its clarity, its cut, etc. Then of course, if you are faced with a choice of two similar gemstones from different locales, you might choose to

acquire the one with an origin that is renowned for producing great pieces of that gem variety, or you may even choose the other piece that is the shining star of an under-rated locale.

Let's discuss the properties that are typically associated with each location, but please do bear in mind the above comments. These are the summary of the huge amount of books I have read, yet my own experience is more in line with the views of George Kunz in that quality and appearance can vary from location to location.

My opinion, that it is not wise to generalise about locales, is based primarily on viewing the gems that flow through my sorting office in Jaipur and those that we sell through our various channels. It is also based on the fact that when I was recently in Zambia I witnessed from one small location in a mine, no bigger than three foot square, a miner unearth the most stunning, clear deep green Emerald, only five minutes later to find two more pieces that were dull and lifeless. The difference can be narrowed even further: it's not just the country, the region, the particular mine, the area within the mine that makes a difference, but the portion of the rough that your gem has been cut from. Only yesterday I was in my cutting facility where we were cutting

some of the finest Amethyst rough we have ever purchased: after making the first slice (a slice is the first cut made to gemstone rough, performed to remove a part of a gem with a big fracture or large feather inclusion), we were left with two totally different grades.

So the information below is more related to the typical types of Sapphires found in each location. It's more like saying you will find more Brits in Britain, more Thais in Thailand and more Indians in India. But if you look in today's cosmopolitan cities, you will realise this type of view is no longer completely valid. It is also important to point out that with today's modern gemstone treatments, such as colour diffusion, these differences are less reliable than they used to be in terms of arriving at a dependable origin, based on appearance alone.

Kashmir Sapphires Regarded by many as the finest Sapphires in the world, they were first discovered in 1879 in the Padar region of Kashmir in Northern India after a landslip allegedly uncovered their occurrence. The Kashmir Sapphire has been known for over a century as "the Jewel of India". Unfortunately, after just a few years of mining, the area became unworkable due to the deposit being in the middle of a politically

unstable area and one fraught with conflict. The matter worsened in 1947 after the partition of the subcontinent, and Kashmir, which is located in the Himalayas some 4500 metres above sea level, has been war torn ever since. So whether it is a result of the conflict or the fact that the mine was depleted within just a few years of its discovery is still not completely understood and remains one of the most talked about topics in gem circles.

Even though the driving force behind its true rarity is not known, at an auction at Christie's in 2007 a 22.66 carat Kashmir Sapphire set in a gold pendant fetched a price of $3,064,000. This equates to around £85,000 per carat!

Kashmir Sapphires are renowned world wide for their almost sleepy appearance. The reason for this is that they have thousands of microscopic inclusions: these cannot be seen by the naked eye, but under a microscope can normally be identified. Also known as flour, these inclusions diffuse the light, providing the Sapphire with its legendary sleepy appearance. The Kashmir Sapphire typically is a very pure blue, with few secondary colours and has a medium tone of 70 to 80%.

Ceylon Sapphire Made famous in

the UK after Princess Diana was given a large Ceylon Sapphire in the centre of her engagement ring and subsequently the ring re-emerged when given to Catherine Middleton on her engagement to Prince William, Ceylon Sapphire is today regarded as the finest Sapphire still being mined in any commercial quantity.

Its hue varies from a medium royal blue to a lighter blue (known as cornflower). The gem often will have some inclusions and slight colour zoning, therefore it is often heat treated to produce a gem that is more appealing to the masses. Its hue varies from almost pure blue to a purplish blue and its tone ranges from approximately 30 to 75% for desirable gems.

Madagascar Sapphires

There are various grades of Sapphire coming out of Madagascar presently. Those from Ilakaka tend to have a nice open colour which has a bluish purplish hue, whilst those from other areas I have seen on the island, such as Andranondambo, tend to have a darker tone. Some pieces coming from the Swiss Bank Mine in Ilakaka, a mine run by John Noel whom I have met several times whilst in Madagascar, often produces pieces that are on par with Sapphires heralding from Burma, Kashmir and Ceylon. Occasionally you

Independent prospectors panning for Sapphire in Madagascar.

will find unusual shaped inclusions in Sapphires from this region and experts have discovered that these are normally either Calcite or Apatite crystals.

Kanchanaburi Sapphire

Famous for its vividly coloured blue Sapphires, the mines at Kanchanaburi and Bo Ploi (also spelt Bo Ploy) also produced the occasional grass green and sunflower yellow Sapphires, as well as their world famous black Spinel. The mines are situated in a jungle valley to the north west of Bangkok, the area is a very popular tourist spot and its bridge was featured in the war film "The Bridge on the River Kwai". The main Sapphire mines are some twenty miles north of the main town. When the first discovery was made in 1918, within months thousands of artisanal miners started digging in an attempt to make their fortunes. Within a very short period, not surprisingly, the mines were all depleted.

In the late 1970s, the gem was once again rediscovered, but this time with JCBs and modern equipment mine owners were able to dig deeper. By the late 1980s they had created possibly the largest alluvial deposit Sapphire mine on the planet and reportedly they had to excavate an average of 19 tonnes of soil to uncover just one carat of gem quality Sapphire! Today, the mines

are once again almost completely exhausted and very little mining is taking place, I met with one local who told me that current miners are having to sift through approximately 50 tonnes of soil to find a single piece of Sapphire.

The quality of Sapphire from the mine can vary from heavily zoned pieces, to pieces that are as open in colour and share a similar clarity to Ceylon Sapphires. In terms of tone, I have seen Bo Ploi Sapphires vary from 60% to 90%. In terms of saturation, Sapphires from the region can be amongst the best on the planet. Whilst Kashmir Sapphires are famed for their silky sleepy appearance, those from Kanchanaburi can sometimes look slightly milky.

As you will see later in this book under "clarity grading", the GIA class Sapphires as a "type II" gemstone, meaning that they normally will feature inclusions. It is for this reason that Kanchanaburi Sapphires are nearly always heat treated. This method perfected in Thailand centuries ago benefits Sapphires from this region in two ways; it reduces the impact of the colour zoning and lessens the visual impact of the inclusions.

Chinese Sapphires

As with most gemstones that originate from China, the amount of data and information we are aware of is very limited. What we do know is that most of the gem quality Sapphires mined in the country come from the Shandong Province, which is situated on the East coast of the country.

As the gem is mined in basaltic or magmatic deposits, they tend to have a tone that is very dark, often in excess of 95%. Under a microscope if you ever find small dark orange inclusions in your Sapphire, there is every chance that these are due to the presence of uranpyrochlore crystals which are often found in Sapphires from the Shandong Province.

Australian Sapphire

Unearthed in New South Wales and Queensland, Australian Sapphires have a tendency to be more of a greenish blue than a pure blue when extracted from the ground. With modern heat treatment techniques, Australian Sapphires are easily transformed into a more pure blue and then sometimes they are miss-sold by ill-informed or unscrupulous dealers as Ceylon Sapphires.

SAPPHIRE
ROUGH & CUT
PH
49854618

Blue Topaz

Blue was once amongst the rarest colour to be seen in Topaz. Today, however, gem experts are able to turn the colourless variety into an array of glorious blues through treatments.

The techniques used are similar to that which naturally occurs in several areas of Brazil, where blue Topaz has been derived from contact from natural radiation of radioactive materials in the earth during their millions of years of formation. The natural blues are far paler than the striking colours that are derived from man made enhancements.There are three stunning Blue Topaz colours: Sky Blue, Swiss Blue and London Blue.

London Blue Topaz: is generally the darkest shade of the Blue Topaz and is incredibly striking. Its tone is normally around 85%, with a hue reminiscent to the deeper areas of the Mediterranean

Sea Swiss Blue: This name is green to Blue Topaz which are lighter than London Blue Topaz but darker in colour than Sky Blue Topaz.

Sky Blue Topaz: is the lightest variety of Blue Topaz (20 to 30% tone) and when they feature great clarity can often look similar to Aquamarine.

Blue Tourmaline is one of the rarest

blues on the planet. This gemstone can be unearthed in array of many different colours, its name is actually arrived from "turmali" which means "mixed precious stones" in Sinhalese. One of the rarest colours for this incredibly special gemstone, a stone that has great transparency even when its saturation of colour is strong, is blue.

There are three tones of blue Tourmaline. The lighter blue is normally referred to as Paraiba Tourmaline, however when mined outside of the Brazilian state of Paraiba the name should only be applied if the gem has the presence of both copper and manganese elements. The tone of Paraiba is around 25 to 35%, which is normally just slightly darker than say a Sky Blue Topaz.

The darker shade of blue Tourmaline is known as Indicolite. Although occasionally it can be found similar to London Blue Topaz, most pieces I have seen are even darker still. The problem with Indicolite is that you often have to really study the piece to find the blue hues; in all but the best lighting conditions it will appear almost black. When you do see a piece that has a dark rich colour, yet light enough to be open, if it has good clarity and is over one carat in weight, it can sometimes demand as much as £1000 per carat in the trade. If the piece has a dark hue approaching 90% or more, the

gem is most likely to be sold to a loose gem collector rather than being set into jewellery.

Sitting nicely between the Paraiba and Indicolite colours is Blue Tourmaline. This tone is normally somewhere between a Swiss Blue Topaz and a London Blue Topaz. Its hue is rarely pure blue and there is normally a secondary hue of green present. This cocktail of colour is truly beautiful. The colour is much more open than Indicolite and whilst the gem looks very pretty indoors, in direct sunlight its appearance transcends from pretty to breathtaking.

Blue Tourmaline is most definitely an outdoor kind of gemstone! Indoors its green hues become more evident and the gem tends to close up and lose some of its transparency. In direct candescent sunlight its blue hues will dominate, its colour opens-up and its appearance is simply world-class.

Over the years I have been fortunate enough to see a handful of Blue Tourmalines and on a recent trip to Brazil I secured a small parcel of wonderful pieces, with text book colour and once faceted they looked truly remarkable. Unfortunately the Cruzeiro Mine near the village of Sâo José Da Safira from where they were unearthed yields very small quantities each year. If the yield was higher then

I truly believe the gem would become more famous than Tanzanite, however the rarity of Blue Tourmaline means that it is exclusively reserved for the true gem collector and enthusiast.

World renowned lapidarist Glenn Lehrer once explained to me that getting your orientation right, when cutting a Blue Tourmaline is crucial. If you cut the gem along the C axis you will end up with a gem that has a more pure blue hue and the percentage of green will be minimised, however the gem will appear a lot darker in tone. However, if you orientate the gem such that the A/B axis is table up, the tone will be lighter but the colour will be more of a greenish blue colour. Therefore whether a gem looks more like a Blue Tourmaline or an Indicolite, often will depend on how the lapidarist decided to orientate the gem and therefore maybe other gem experts are after all correct by just referring to all intensely coloured Blue Tourmalines as Indicolite.

84

Bolivia

Currently the only known location of a multi coloured transparent appearance created entirely by nature, with a level of brilliance and beauty that will often leave you speechless.

Currently the only consistent source of Ametrine in the world is found at the Anahi Mine located in the province of Santa Cruz in Eastern Bolivia. Just like the mines in neighbouring Brazil, Bolivia also provides naturally occurring Citrine and dark, vivid Amethyst.

Ametrine, which is half Citrine and half Amethyst, first appeared set in jewellery in the 1970s. But soon after its discovery, some gem experts claimed that the gem's unusual bi-colour effect was artificially created in laboratories and as a result, the gem lost popularity. Once it was proven that this was not the case and the bi-colour was in fact due to a natural phenomenon occurring only in this one region of the world, demand for this unusual gem started to increase.

As the gem is primarily mined in just one location, from time to time the owners of the Anahi mine seem to deliberately cut back on excavation so as to ensure there is less supply for the gem than there is demand.

Boutique Collection

A contemporary collection of stunningly faceted, vivid gemstones, with precision setting and exquisite attention to detail.

Designed with passion
Created with precision

Bracelets and Bangles

A bracelet is an item of jewellery that is worn around the wrist and can be made out of various materials, including silver, gold, plastic and metal. The name bracelet comes from the Latin word "brachile" which means "of the arm."

Egypt is believed to be the country which invented the original bracelet, but not as we know it today. Egyptians would use bones, stones and wood, strung together with animal hair.

The earliest bracelets are believed to date back as far as 2500BC. When women wore bracelets in this period

it was primarily to show how wealthy their husbands were. It wasn't until approximately 200BC that bracelets were first believed to have been worn purely for personal adornment.

There are different types of bracelets that are known and worn today, one of which is the charm bracelet, which archaeological discoveries have found were worn by the Pharaohs.

Charms were believed to bring good luck, and men would use any materials they could beg, borrow or steal, with the belief that once they had been made into a charm they would ward off any evil spirits.

Bracelets will always be a part of our culture and as fashion changes so do the different styles of bracelets. For example, the Romans and Greeks wore short sleeved shirts, making the wearing of bracelets on the upper and lower arm popular. In Victorian times, Marcasite bracelets set with big gems such as Jasper and Jet were highly fashionable. Today, gents' Titanium bracelets are fashionable and ladies' charm bracelets are back in fashion and hotter than ever before.

Brazil Possibly the largest treasure chest of gemstones on the planet.

The fifth largest country in the world, Brazil is one of the most important countries in terms of both volume and diversity of gemstones unearthed every year. Today the country is best known for its Amethyst, Agate, Emerald, Tourmaline, Topaz and Quartz; however until the discovery of Diamonds in South Africa in the 1860s, historically Brazil was the world's largest supplier.

The country is not just about volume production, it is also home to some real treasures that can be found hardly

Christ the Redeemer, Rio de Janeiro, Brazil.

anywhere else in the world. The three most famous being its stunning Imperial Topaz, its deep, vivid coloured Santa Maria Aquamarine and its very rare Paraiba Tourmaline.

Over a hundred different gemstones have been discovered in Brazil: in addition to those already mentioned Opal, Amblygonite, Garnets and Morganite of a very high quality are also mined.

Most of the mining is carried out by prospectors and artisanal miners and considering the country is so vast, only a handful of large scale mining corporations are operating there.

In terms of contribution to the world's supply of gemstones by volume, it is estimated that a quarter of all faceted gems in the world each year originate from Brazil. That's quite amazing when you consider that three of the largest selling gemstones, Diamonds, Rubies and Sapphires, are only mined on a very small scale.

According to official data supplied by the IBGM (Brazilian Agency for the Promotion of Export and Investment) just four out of the 26 states in Brazil are responsible for 97% of its gemstone production, namely Minas Gerais, Mato Grosso, Bahia and Rio Grande do Sul.

Brazil: a gemstone treasure chest.

Minas Gerais Gemstone mining is so important in terms of the economy in this state, that even its name means General Mining. It's impossible to know for sure how many people are involved in the mining industry in Minas Gerais, as due to very high taxation on gemstones, much of the mining is carried out illegally. However, IBGM state that over 100 companies are involved in official mining and over 300 companies are cutting and polishing gemstones. It is believed that as many as 170,000 families have their income supported by gemstone activities in this one region alone!

The State of Minas Gerais can then be broken down into seven important geological regions:

- Pedra Azul for Topaz and Aquamarine.
- Padre Paraiso where Aquamarine, Chrysoberyl, Helidor and Topaz can be found.
- Conselheiro Pena for Tourmaline, Aquamarine, Morganite and Kunzite.
- Santa Maria de Itabira where Emerald, Alexandrite and Aquamarine of incredible quality have been unearthed.
- Sao Jose da Safira for Tourmaline, Morganite and Garnet.
- Malacacheta for Chrysoberyl including its colour change variety Alexandrite.
- Aracuai for Tourmaline, Aquamarine, Morganite and Topaz.

In most of these gem bearing districts, the finds are normally associated with granitic rocks and hydrothermal deposits.

In addition to those already mentioned, Minas Gerais also yields small pockets of Hiddenite, Scapolite, Brazilianite, Petalite, Amblygonite and low grade Ruby and Sapphire.

Bahia Although Minas Gerais produces more cut gemstones than the state of Bahia, in terms of gemstone rough, Bahia is second only to Rio Grande do Sul. Much of the gem trading is conducted in Salvador and the rough is then normally sent to cities such

as Jaipur for cutting and polishing. Some of the most important gems in the region are Emerald, Amethyst and Aquamarine. But how about the following for a treasure chest: Alexandrite, Amazonite, Andalusite, Apatite, Chrysoberyl, Citrine, Diamond, Dumortierite, Emerald, Fluorite, Jasper, Malachite, Morganite, Ruby, Rutile Quartz, Sapphire, Topaz, Tourmaline, Turquoise and Zircon have also been discovered.

During the 19th century many Diamond prospectors were busy mining in a region known as Chapa Diamantina. In an attempt to protect the beautiful National Park in Chapa, in 1996 the government placed a ban on Diamond mining and now Bahia is all about colour!

Now here is a bit of trivia: where are some of the world's oldest Emeralds discovered? Well Emeralds in the famous Swat Valley in Pakistan are estimated to be around just 23 million years old (very young in gem terms), those from Chivor and other areas in Colombia date back to around 65 million years ago. Prior to that, Emeralds in the Minas Gerais and Santa Terezinha in Goias were formed approximately 500 million years ago. However, in Carnaiba and Socoto in the state of Bahia, Emeralds were

formed around 2 billion years ago! That's old!

Rio Grande Do Sul For Agate and Amethyst, Rio Grande do Sul (the most southern state in Brazil) is the most important gemstone location on the planet and over 90% of the state's gemstone revenue is derived from these. Rio Grande do Sul is also the largest gemstone mining state in Brazil and most of the gem trading is done in the municipality of Soledade.

Much of the world's supply of Citrine is also mined here, however it comes out of the ground as Amethyst, which is then heat treated and the high concentration of iron found naturally in the gems from this region oxidise, turning the gem an incredible glowing sunflower yellow.

Mato Grosso & Goias Made famous for its discovery of Emerald in the northern region of the state in 1981, Mato Grosso also has small deposits of Diopside, Garnet and Zircon.

Over the past few decades, the Santa Terezinha mines in the state of Goias have provided some of the most important sources of Emerald in Brazil. Unfortunately, the Santa Terezinha mine, from which Coloured Rocks sourced its beautiful Emeralds from in

early 2010, is no longer in production. These Emeralds exhibit a greenish dark blue/yellowish pale green pleochroism which is characteristic of their distinguished beauty. Emeralds by their very nature are prone to natural inclusions, so look out for the occasional 'Terezinha Black Spot': the local miners claim it brings good fortune and good luck!

In addition to the four big mining states of Brazil, there are two more worthy of a mention:

Paraiba Even if they have never seen it firsthand, there is not a gem dealer worth his salt that will not at least have heard of Paraiba Tourmaline. The gem received its name as it was first discovered in 1988 in the state of Paraiba in a region known as Mina da Batalha.

Unfortunately, very little Paraiba Tourmaline has ever been discovered in Paraiba and very few pieces from the initial find weigh over half a carat! Today, for Paraiba Tourmaline we have to turn to Mozambique to discover the gem, but these deposits have all but dried up too! Unless new sources of Paraiba Tourmaline are discovered, I would like to suggest a very beautiful alternative from the state of Paraiba: Amblygonite. Not only is the gemstone

found in the same region, visually it is strikingly similar: demonstrating a blend of swimming pool blues and sea green hues.

Piaui -*Pronounced 'pee-Ow-Ee'.*
The Opals from this region as a general rule tend to be more 'pinfire' as opposed to 'broadflash'. If you are new to this gem terminology, basically speaking 'pinfire' is, as its name suggests, the appearance of multi coloured pin sized spots appearing across the Opal as it moves. In Piaui Opals it is more common to see this type of effect rather than 'broadflash', where the colours tend to flow into one another like water over an oily surface.

As well as unearthing Opals looking similar to their Australian counterpart, Piaui is also home to some wonderful Fire Opals. During 1997 there was even a discovery of Blue Fire Opal in the state.

After Australia, Brazil is probably the world's second largest supplier of Opal. The most important contributor is the municipality of Pedro II, which lies in the north east of the state of Piaui. Opals have been discovered in the alluvial deposits of several rivers in the region; notably the Corrente and the Dos Matos.

Whilst it is possible to find white and black Opals in the region that feature the same kaleidoscopic colours as those discovered at Lightning Ridge and Coober Pedy in Australia, Piaui is also home to a range of single coloured, opaque Opals.

Brazilian Collection

Not for the shy or reserved, exclusively designed for those who want their jewellery to get them noticed.

THE BRAZILIAN COLLECTION

Brazil Feature

Gem mining adventure in Brazil

Sunrise in Rio de Janeiro.

This special feature on my trip to Brazil in May 2011 is rather extensive, but I thought you might like to know more about how gemstones are mined and traded in Brazil.

This trip started on the 1st of May 2011 with a four day conference in Rio de Janeiro hosted by the ICA (International Colored Gemstone Association). The ICA is the largest organisation in the world for coloured gem miners, dealers and bodies such as the GIA, CIBJO and The Responsible Jewellery Council. Every two years we hold a major conference; this year's event received delegates from 42 different countries. The main theme for the conference was ethical mining and as I sit on the Fair Trade and Ethical Mining Committee for the ICA I was invited to be a guest speaker.

As soon as the conference finished my son Matthew and I started our tour of Brazilian gem mines with a visit to the Southern state of Rio Grande Do Sul, to check out where many of our Amethysts and Agates are sourced. The journey South took in three flights, first stopping at Sao Paulo, then Florianopolis and finally Chapéco. This was the start of ten days of a real gem hunting venture: part of our trip to the larger mines was to be organised by the ICA and then a couple of my

Miner at the Pedernira mine pushing dirt cart back to the underground mine.

crazy Brazilian friends were going to fly and drive us around to some of the less formal mining areas.

Brazil plays a very important role in the gem world. As the fifth largest country in the world, Brazil is divided into 26 states. Although a handful of different gemstones are unearthed in a few northern states, the vast majority are discovered between the centre of the country down to the southern state of Rio Grande do Sul. Therefore, whilst I would love to have gone into the Amazon jungle in the North of the country, we were going to focus this adventure to the south.

After a trip to Tucson earlier in the year where both of our video cameras decided to stop working, this time Matt and I were loaded down with three video cameras and a bunch of SLR's. The drive from to Chapeco to Ametista do Sul took around two hours. During the drive we crossed the Uruguai River which separates the two states of Santa Catarina and Rio Grande do Sul. The river is hugely significant to the region as it supplies water and electricity to both Southern Brazil and Argentina.

Rio Grande do Sul was named by the Portuguese who believed on arriving in the East of the country that they had settled alongside a large river: the

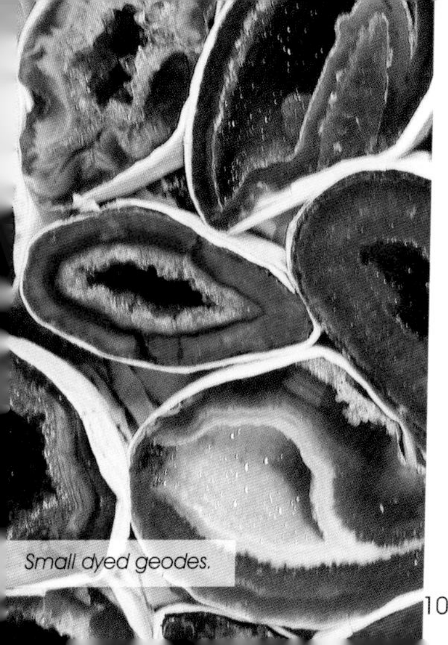
Small dyed geodes.

literal translation is “large river of the south”.

Our mining visits were to be focused around mines in the town of Ametista do Sul: although today the number of operating mines has dwindled, the area is still a major player in the supply of Amethyst. The town has a population of 8000 and luckily for us the young mayor (he became mayor at the age of just 24) Silvio Poncio also owned several mines. Even better he informed us that he also ran a vineyard: for me the trip was getting better and better! First Silvio took us to one of his mines that was no longer in production. He explained that the tunnels we were

about to enter were all horizontal and once we descended the initial 40 metres the mine shafts all ran flat. The vein in which the Amethyst is discovered is just three metres high. Miners at first use explosives, then as they get closer to the area where they are likely to find Amethyst geodes change to pneumatic drills and finally when they discover a geode use a hammer and chisel to remove it. Whilst in the Cordilheira mine, one of Silvio's miners offered me the opportunity to try and extract a small geode. The basaltic rock was incredibly tough and after just a few minutes I started to appreciate what a difficult job mining Amethyst geodes was.

Whilst Amethyst unearthed in the north of Brazil is discovered in pegmatites, in Rio Grande do Sul they are all formed in geodes (see geodes). Rather than go through all of the time and effort of removing a geode, only then to cut it open to find that there is no Amethyst inside, or that the crystals are too small or included to be of any real value, once they discover a geode embedded in the host basaltic they drill a hole into it and using a probe on a long flexible rod place it into the geode to see if it is worthy of carefully and painstakingly extracting.

Many geodes are sold directly at the opening of the pit to locals who then

Extinct Amethyst mine converted into huge wine cellar.

go and extract the Amethyst from the geodes. Most of these gem dealers are small family businesses that process the geodes in their back garden or tin roofed garage. After cutting the Amethyst free from the geode they cob it (hit with a hammer) to remove any areas that are fractured or heavily included. Next, if the colour is good it is packed and ready to be sold to gem cutters in the bigger towns. If, however, the gem in the geode is not of a good colour, many of these families have their own furnaces where they will heat treat the Amethyst in hope of turning it into Citrine. These are not the same modern furnaces that we see in Jaipur and Bangkok: they are very basic and traditional, but with experience comes expertise. These local gem families know exactly what temperature and for what length of time to expose the Amethyst, all differing depending on its original hue and tone and from which mine shaft it came from. Silvio told me that the average geode was heated for 12 hours and to a temperature of 460 degrees Celsius.

Some rough can also be transformed to cognac, whisky or beer quartz (all descending in tone), whilst other Amethyst from different mines can be turned into delightful Green Amethyst. These treatments though are more complex than something you can do in

a furnace in your back yard and require gamma radiation treatment.

In Brazil there are three companies that carry out this treatment and they are located in Rio de Janeiro, Belo Horizonte and São Palo. This treatment is totally safe and unlike the radiation treatment used with Topaz where it has to settle for six months, the gamma radiated gems can be released after just a few days. At this stage though, the crystals have not yet changed to their new identity and they now need to be heat treated to finish their transformation.

Anyway, back to the Cordilheira Amethyst mine: as I mentioned above the mine is now exhausted, however Silvio realising that the temperature remained constant at 17 degrees all year round - a temperature similar to the tunnels in Reims France where most of the world's Champagne was historically stored - has converted his Amethyst mine into a giant wine cellar. For me, this was a remarkable experience: there are so many myths and legends surrounding Amethyst, but one that everyone knows is how it is supposed to prevent you from getting drunk and here is a young and innovative gem miner-cum-mayor-cum-vintner who is cleverly combining his assets. Within a few

years he wants to go one stage further and turn the winery/gem mine into a tourist destination and if this happens I will recommend the trip to anyone who collects gemstones, especially if you also have a taste for fine wines.

After visiting the mines and the local families working on extracting the Amethyst from the geodes and heat treating them in their garages and lean-tos, Marcelo Bernardes (a gem dealer in Brazil) explained how the community is facing a real issue at the moment. In China the growing middle and upper classes have fallen in love with geodes as ornaments, so much so that the value of them has doubled in less than a year. Whilst this is good news for the miners, most of whom work in small co-operatives, it is not good news for those who have specialised in purchasing geodes to extract the gemstones to supply to gem cutting houses for generations. Right now, with the massive hike in price many are looking for a new livelihood and several families have already uprooted and left the town for good.

I asked Marcelo, who is one of the most respected Amethyst cutters and gem dealers in Brazil, and what he thought the future was for Ametista do Sol: he believed that either the price of loose Amethyst will need to increase

Inside the Igreja Sao Gabriel Church.

by at least double in the trade, or it will no longer be available as more and more people in Asia start collecting the geodes. He also believes that as Rio Grande do Sul is such a major player in the world for Amethyst, as supply continues to dry up it will increase the price of the gemstone from other locations around the planet.

After visiting several mines, Silvio wanted to show us a local church that the community built between 2004 and 2006. It was an amazing experience. The local mining community had all come together to support the project and had donated millions and millions of Amethyst stones (all be

it of a low commercial grade) to line the entire walls of the church. It was breathtakingly beautiful. Matt - my son and cameraman - asked if I could do a spontaneous piece for the documentary we were filming during our trip, but for once I had to tell him to just sit back and soak up the experience; it was mesmerising. For centuries Amethyst has had a close link with the Catholic Church and here was the Igreja Sao Gabriel Church completely lined with rough cut gems. The altar was even a huge geode, the font used for baptism was also a geode, and the back of the priest's chair was two huge Amethysts flanking a row of Citrine.

The next day we travelled to Soledade, to meet Mr Agate: that's not his real name of course but Mauricio Lodi runs one of the largest Agate cutting and treatment companies on the planet. All of his gems come from near the banks of the beautiful "Salto do Jacui"; this remote location is famed for producing some of the finest patterned Agates available anywhere. Most of the Agates formed at this location are inside miniature geodes with sizes rarely exceeding two feet. Many of them completely fill the geode, whilst others come to rest with a small hole in the centre which is often lined with Drusy. Over the time I spent with Mauricio, I can honestly say that I saw

every natural colour possible across the collection of Agates he had in stock. However, as the hues, tones and saturation varied in every single piece, many are dyed to provide the gem with a more saturated and repeatable colour.

Mauricio explained how each colour uses a different treatment; his blues and greens were dyed at a temperature in excess of 200 degrees and the colour was permanent. Pinks and purples however had to be dyed at lower temperatures and he warned that if left in exposed sunlight for excessive periods they would fade slightly. I thought this was worthy as a mention just in case I ever started selling his outdoor Agate wind charms! The colours of the dyes have intense saturation and yet somehow the patterns are not masked, but appear to be more defined.

As well as being possibly the world's largest supplier of Agates, Mauricio is also known as Mr. Geode. His geode production is incredible, with some pieces being over ten feet tall and one piece I saw weighed over three tonnes! If you ever visit Gems TV's UK television studios, the two huge pieces in our reception were sawn and prepared by one of Mauricio's skilled employees. For more information on

The famous Iguaçu waterfall.

geodes see the feature in book G.

Whilst I was in the area I met up with Joe an old friend of mine whose business partner had discovered a new Fire Opal in the area and asked if I wanted to buy their run of mine (a run of mine is effectively a commitment to take whatever they extract over a period of time and at a set price). The colours were amazing, the clarity was as good as I have seen from Mexico and therefore I agreed to take everything they currently had in inventory.

Next we went to do a spot of sightseeing at the famous Iguaçu waterfalls. These are situated at the border between Paraguay, Brazil and Argentina and are without doubt one of the most mesmerising landscapes on planet Earth. After seeing the falls from the Brazilian side we crossed the border into Argentina to film from the other side. This was even more breathtaking. After a day of chilling it was back to business and Matt and I flew to Bel Horizona the capital of Minas Gerais to go to a barbecue being held by gem expert Marcelo Bernardes at which many important members of the ICA were attending.

The next morning we decided to split up: Matt would go and film with my good buddy Glenn Lehrer at the

Imperial Topaz mine at Ouro Preto.

world's most famous Imperial Topaz mine at Ouro Preto, and I would fly to Minas Gerais and spend one day sourcing gems in Valaderes and one day in Tefino Antoni. These two neighbouring towns (well, one hundred miles is pretty much a neighbour in Brazil) are the country's equivalent of Jaipur, India Bangkok, and Thailand when it comes to the trading, cutting and exporting of gemstones. A very good friend of mine, Joas Salvador, was going to take care of me for my two day visit. The first day I spent looking at a parcel of Morganite that Joas Salvador had treated for us then applied the first cut which is known as a "preform". Let me explain this in a little more detail: Joas had been collecting the rough from a particular mine in Mozambique for around one year. It was then sent to Brazil where Joas Salvador's team sliced and preformed the gem. A preform cut provides the gemstone with its outline shape.

As this collection was of a very high grade, Joas Salvador decided to send the parcel to a laboratory in Thailand to have it irradiated. Next it was shipped back to Brazil to undergo its final heat treatment. That's a lot of travelling and expense, but when you deal with fine quality gemstones, it's worth making sure that the end result is the best you

What's claimed to be the worlds largest pair of uncut Morganites. Weighing in at 22.4KG and 33.5KG.

can get. Many cutting houses don't perform the final heat treating process, but without it I am told the colour of the Morganite becomes unstable.

I sat with Joas and negotiated a deal for his entire collection: whilst he was happy with the hard price I bargained, he did say that it would not be repeatable in the future, as the price of the rough had gone through the roof due to increased demand for the gemstone in Asia, and also there had been a steep rise in the cost of mining. So we sealed the parcel, filled in all of the complex export paperwork and prepared them for shipping to our cutting house in Jaipur. This is the exciting part for me and also the big gamble: I have to estimate what the end carat weight will be after we have faceted the gems. Whilst it is a little easier buying preforms than buying the rough straight from the mine, (where your yield can be anywhere from 3% to 50%), as Morganite is an expensive gem if my yield is less than 65% then my calculations on value become incorrect and will most likely lose money.

So when you next see one of our beautiful Mozambique Morganites, just think how much work has gone into first prospecting for the gem, then mining it, then preforming, heating,

Lunchtime over, back to work.

irradiating and once again heating, and that's all before one of our highly skilled lapidarists even cuts the first facet.

Next, Joas was excited to show me a brand new discovery from the North of Brazil at an area known as the Para estate, close to the mine Sao Geraldo do Araguaia. As he opened up his woven grey sack in which he kept his samples from the mine, the sunlight caught the top of one of the crystals and I saw golden snowflakes in an ice cube. Well not quite, this was a transparent quartz that had two mineral inclusions trapped inside, the most abundant I am sure is Pyrite and the

second inclusion, we are going to have to wait until I get a laboratory report to correctly identify. Joas needed some cash to go back and carry on extracting the gem and I agreed to underpin his next round of mining.

The next morning I visited Saint Clair Fonseca Júnior, he is one of the most well known miners in Minas Gerais. Saint-Clair specialises in prospecting and then extracting Tourmalines, not just in Brazil but also in Mozambique. We sat and discussed his mining operation and I asked him what pockets, (an area in a mine where gems are found), his team had found recently. Saint-Clair took the key to the safe, disappeared for a couple of minutes and returned with a small parcel of bi-coloured Tourmaline. Each piece had really nice transparency and when I mentioned this, Saint-Clair said he had one small parcel that was even better a few weeks before, but the Chinese buyers arrived and bought the entire production: at a staggering price of over a thousand dollars per carat! That was certainly a new benchmark for this stone as far as I was concerned, but later in the trip I spoke to one miner who told me the Chinese were now paying up to $2000 for top grade Bi- Coloured Tourmaline.

Miner's village near the Pedeneira mine.

Whilst the parcel I was looking at was indeed beautiful, as Saint-Clair and myself believe in long term mutually beneficial business relationships he offered me a very good price. I was extremely happy as I had not been able to source any really nice quality Bi-Coloured Tourmaline for over three years. He asked if I would like to film at his mining operation whilst I was in the area and we agreed to visit later in the week once Matt had rejoined me.

Next he asked if I wanted to see the biggest Morganite in the world: I told him that would not be possible as to my knowledge I already owned the largest piece. Saint-Clair smiled, walked over to the side of his office where there were two small wooden stools with large dishcloths covering something resting on top. Like a magician revealing a rabbit at the end of a trick, Saint-Clair whipped off the cloth and I froze to the spot. Speechless, unable to comprehend what lay before me, were two huge pieces of rough Morganite. The colour was amazing, the size was unimaginable and once I took a lamp to it, I could see that it was a fairly clean crystal. The larger piece weighed 33.5KG. I asked Saint-Clair if they had been treated in anyway, he told me that when he first got the stones the colour was not as beautiful, so he left them outside in his back yard for

a couple of months and through the natural radiation of the sun, the pieces transformed into the vivid colour they now are.

I asked what he was going to do with them and he said that our mutual friend Glenn had made an offer for one of the pieces at the Tucson Gem Show back in January and I recommended that this was probably the most likely home for them. Glenn is one of the world's leading gemstone carvers and I said that I could just imagine the sort of design he could do. If Glenn didn't purchase them I suggested Saint-Clair maybe offer them to a museum.

Before I left I asked him why nobody was unearthing any Paraiba Tourmaline in Mozambique, Saint-Clair said that they had recently found a new pocket at his mine and the quality was superb, "would you like to see a few pieces" he asked, "is the Pope Catholic?" I responded. Wow, these pieces were perfect, possessing great clarity and a text book swimming pool colour. Then the bad news, Saint-Clair was asking two thousand dollars a carat: I tried to negotiate but he was not even entertaining the idea of dropping his price. I asked why the price had soared and once again the answer was the same as I had been hearing all year long, there is a huge demand in Asia

right now for this treasure also.

The stones were exceptional though, but in these situations as a gem buyer I have to make sure my head over rules my heart. Also as one of the larger buyers in the market, it's important that I don't set a precedent with miners, if I had shown any remote interest when he mentioned the price, news would have spread around the industry that we were entertaining the idea of paying the new prices higher.

A gemstone buyer negotiating with a miner is like two people playing poker: neither reveals their hand. Sometimes the seller starts incredibly high to judge the buyer's reaction, sometimes the buyer starts ridiculously low to get the game started. All of the time both parties commenting on the quality of the goods; the seller always claiming that it is an exceptionally good price for the quality he has on offer, always saying that the gems are getting harder to find and how his cost of mining is ever going up, the buyer arguing how his customers will not pay the price and therefore he cannot buy it anywhere near the price the seller wants. Always both players leave the door open by not making any absolute claims. But in this instance I could sense Saint-Clair was very serious about the price, so I said I was not going to even make an

offer. "OK Steve, why don't I invite you out to the mine in Mozambique, you can come and film and see for yourself how little is coming out of the ground and then maybe you might start increasing your offers a little". Going into a Paraiba mine, with one of the industry's leading experts on the gem, was an offer I could not refuse and we hope to make the trip sometime during the summer.

That afternoon Joas and I left Valaderes and drove northeast for approximately 100 miles to the town of Teofilo Otoni (pronounced Tee-af-alo Otoni). The road was similar to an English A road in width, but that is where the similarity ended. It twisted and wound along beautiful rolling scenery, the volcanic red soil which can be seen across virtually the entire south of Brazil providing the perfect base for huge green forests to flourish. Teofilo Otoni is a very important gem town in Minas Gerais and an area where many of the locally mined Aquamarines, Emeralds, Alexandrites, Tourmalines and Chrysoberyl are traded.

Joas had arranged with a friend of his to use his office for the afternoon and had already put the word out on the street that I would be coming to town to source gems. By the time we had arrived, there was already a long

line of gem miners, cutters and traders waiting to try and sell their goods. This is very similar to the way we often buy in Jaipur, however the queue was much more orderly than in India. One other difference is these people were not the principles. In India it's normally the actual owner of the gems that arrives to sell his stones, even if they have to queue for four hours, a sale makes it worth their while. In Teofilo Otoni owners tend to send someone to display their gems for them so that they don't have to waste an afternoon in a line! It's a little frustrating though as all deals need a phone call to the owner to see if they accept the offer.

I saw around 60 to 70 deals over the afternoon and we sealed the final one at around 8pm and started our two hour drive back to Valadares. One of the main gems I was looking for was Indicolite: unfortunately nobody had more than a dozen pieces in a single parcel. This was a little frustrating as I only managed to find 27 pieces over a six hour buying session. I did however get a few amazing deals on Aquamarine and a very nice pair of matching pear cut Paraiba Tourmalines.

The next morning Joas drove me three hours to the Belmont Emerald Mine, I arrived at 9am and met up with the owner Marcelo Ribeiro. He explained

Searching for Tourmaline at the Pederneira mine.

the history behind the mine, which was first started by his grandfather Mauro Ribeiro in 1979.

The Belmont mine is probably the second largest open pit coloured gem mine on the planet and their underground mine is certainly the largest I have ever visited. The mine is located in an Emerald-rich region called Itabira and incredibly well managed, with state of the art equipment. For more details on this mine see the Belmont mine feature.

Friday morning we woke early: it was the last day of our Brazilian adventure and we had saved the best until last. This is the day we were going to visit Saint-Clair's Pederneira Mine and the most important Tourmaline deposit of the past 40 years at the Cruzeiro Mine.

Once you leave the main road outside of Valaderes you have to travel around 70 miles on a very bumpy dust track to reach the Tourmaline-rich pegmatites. The track is so rough that it took us over three hours to reach our destination, although we didn't mind too much as the scenery was spectacular with cattle farms and ranches set into the hillside along virtually the entire journey.

Before we arrived at the mines, we stopped at a little village called Sâo José Da Safira, here for many years gemstones from the surrounding hill

sides have been traded. Joas told me, "I was born and raised in the village, most gem trading gets done on a Friday so that the miners have enough money to buy food for their families for the weekend". It's a really quaint place; as we arrived the local school were on their lunch break and all of the children were wearing the school tee-shirt which had a huge sketch of a gemstone in the centre. All the houses were painted bright vivid colours to represent the various colours that Tourmaline can be found, and being a Friday we could sense an air of anticipation of deals that would be done that afternoon. As we were leaving the village we saw two miners bringing their rough gemstones into the village in sacks hanging from the saddles of their horse.

Within just a mile or so from the village you start your ascent into the mountains. The road turns back into a bumpy dust road after a brief but welcome spell of tarmac through the village. As you climb, the views across the valley continue to grow more beautiful. It's exactly the image I had had in my head of what I thought the Brazilian countryside would look like. Dense forests, thick under-growth and the relaxing sounds of crickets made the ordeal of our journey pass more quickly, however I was starting to feel slightly bruised from bouncing up and

The colourful village life at Safira

Matt filming in the gemstone village of Sao Jose da Safira

down for three hours and constantly banging myself as I tried to capture the scenery through my camera lens. We finally arrived at the Pederneira Mine and Saint-Clair was there to meet us. He first of all showed us around the living quarters where the staff reside whilst they are in the mountain mining, I can imagine the fewer times they have to leave the mine the better as after a hard day at the mine face, digging and shovelling, the last thing you would want to do is travel on a bumpy road home.

I asked Saint-Clair what the significance of the tower was outside the mine: he explained that over the past few years, every time they had discovered a new pocket, after mining it for a few days they were robbed. Now they post armed gunmen in the towers to look after the mine. He is not the only mine owner to have the same problem and recently many of them clubbed together to make a clearing on the hillside so you can land a small plane. Now when there is a good discovery they try and fly the gems out of the mine on the day they are unearthed. He also explained how the police were starting to be very helpful and whenever they had a good day's mining just one call to the head of police and he would send two armed officers up the mountain to the mine. In fact whilst we were there, the police

escorted us from one mine to the next and stayed guarding our vehicles.

Back to the mine: the opening is about 100 metres from the summit of the mountain (Matt tells me that geologically speaking it's actually a large hill and not a mountain), a miniature railway type track leads to the opening which is around five foot high and four feet wide. Ventilation and lighting is provided by a generator and once inside you can't help but feel like you have just stepped into the scene of an Indiana Jones movie. After about one hundred metres of the tunnel running horizontally, the mine shaft abruptly starts to descend at a 45 degree angle. Saint-Clair tried to explain to me in lay-man terms how the miners try and follow the vein of a pegmatite. Similar to Emerald mining, the reaction zone where you are likely to find Tourmalines sits alongside the pegmatites. The slight difference being that quality Tourmalines tend to be found in miniature cave like openings known as pockets, alongside the pegmatite.

Once the miners start to see pieces of black Tourmaline in the rock face they know there is every possibility that there is a pocket in the vicinity. When the indicators are found the miners stop using dynamite and move to the

more conventional method of hammer and chisel. They drill holes into the rock face surrounding the indicator and if the drill goes through into a hole or if water spurts out, they know they have found a pocket. Saint-Clair also explained how that normally if they found small pieces of Rubellite or Indicolite in the tunnel, then it meant there was every possibility of finding more of that gem in the approximate vicinity.

Next it was my turn to do some work and I started to help the miners shovel the day's chippings and rocks into a dirt cart. The thin air combined with the underground humidity causes you to break out in an unstoppable sweat as soon as you start manual work. Once we loaded the cart we attached it to a cable and a pulley system began to grind as the cart was pulled up the steep incline. At the top, we unattached it and I then pushed it along the flat. Unfortunately, the flat ground is not completely flat and descends slightly towards the pit entrance. Matt was in front of the cart walking backwards so he could film my efforts, but as we neared the entrance the cart started to pick up speed. I was trying my best to slow it down but with all of the rocks inside I couldn't hold it back, I shouted to Matt to get out of the way but there was nowhere for him to go, to the left

30m underground Saint-Clair and Steve Bennett

of the cart's handle I saw the brake so gave it an almighty pull and the entire contents of the cart spilled onto the track. What I had assumed was a brake was in fact a lever which opened the front of the cart making it easy for the miners to empty it once out of the mine. But here we now were, with a mixture of rocks, chippings and potentially one or two fine gemstones spilt all over the track. The miners came to the rescue with a few shovels and between us we spent ages refilling the cart, making sure that there was not a single ounce of rock left on the floor. Saint Clair and his miners all thought it was hilarious how my first attempt at simply guiding the cart along a track to the mine entrance had ended in failure.

Unfortunately, today was not our lucky day and the cart had no gem-quality material inside. As a miner wheeled it back into the mine to repeat the process, I stayed outside the shaft as Saint-Clair told me stories of the great discoveries they had made over the last 10 years.

After a well deserved late lunch prepared by Saint Clair's wife and daughter, we set off with our police escort to the Cruzeiro Mine. This mine opened in 1935, not as a gemstone mine but as a mica mine. All around the perimeter of the mine you can see small

Colourful mining village near Cruzeiro.

pieces of mica. Before glass windows became the norm, many people used mica and during the Second World War the mineral was used to line the fuselage of fighter planes. It wasn't until the 1970s after the discovery of Rubellite that the shafts were converted into a commercial gemstone mine. Throughout the 1970s and 1980s the mine was one of the best producing Tourmaline mines on the planet.

Unfortunately the two brothers who owned the mine were tragically killed when their small plane crashed. Literally overnight the rest of the family had to take on the huge responsibility of running the mine. And what a good job they are doing of it, the day we were there they had extracted five or six pieces of of gem quality Rubellite: it's not just another gemstone industry myth that Cruzeiro yields some of the finest Rubellites and Blue Tourmalines on the planet, I have seen it with my own eyes: it really does. The mine's geologist took us down various tunnels and shafts and explained the local geology. Once we got back above ground level, Douglas showed me their washing plant. This is not like the big commercial Emerald mines of Gemfields and Belmont, but a huge half barrel the size of a paddling pool and about three foot tall, in which the bags of rough stones and mud are

The view over the Doce Valley

poured into a round mesh tray and the miner begins to wash in a rotating pattern. Douglas invited me to have a go for myself: he poured the extracted material into my tray and I began the action. After about 30 seconds I lifted the tray out of the water and bingo! There in the centre of my mesh sat a small vividly red piece of rough Rubellite. Unfortunately after faceting it would probably weight less than a quarter of a carat, but that didn't matter to me, I felt quite emotional as here I was at an historic gemstone mine, one I had read so much material on, a mine that I had heard gem traders waxing lyrical about for years and I had just played part of the process and helped in discovering a small piece of history. For more information on the mine read the feature on the Cruzeiro Mines.

"So my time in Brazil was over. I had met many amazing gem experts along the way, visited the most important Tourmaline deposits in the world and even spent several days having a go at gem mining for myself.

Brazil is undoubtedly one of the most diverse gem mining countries I have visited and it won't be long before I return on my next gem hunting adventure."

HIGH PRIEST IN ROBES AND BREASTPLATE

Breastplate of Aaron

It is believed that the tradition of birthstones arose from the Breastplate of Aaron, a ceremonial religious garment that was set with twelve gemstones.

The gems represented the twelve tribes of Israel, which also corresponded with the twelve signs of the zodiac and the twelve months of the year.

It is referred to in the book of Exodus in the Old Testament of the Bible and was made for Moses' brother Aaron and his sons to be worn as a garment so they could serve as priests.

Taken from Exodus: “It is to be square – a span long and a span wide and folded double. Then mount four rows of precious stones on it. In the first row there shall be a Ruby, a Topaz and a Beryl; in the second row a Turquoise, a Sapphire and an Emerald; in the third row a Jacinth, an Agate and an Amethyst; in the fourth row a Chrystolite, an Onyx and a Jasper”.

(28:16-17). The Breastplate of Aaron is of interest to gem lovers as it is an early account of the use of gemstones as both decoration and symbolism. The breastplate is described in the Bible as the “Breastplate of Judgement” or the “Breastplate of Decision”. As they used ancient biblical descriptions for the gems, unfortunately it is difficult for translators to determine several of those used with exact certainty. Therefore, the list of gems varies slightly depending on which translation is used.

Brilliance The internal life witnessed inside a gemstone.

There are three main terms used to describe the way light interacts with a gemstone: 'lustre', the surface reflection of light; 'dispersion', when light inside certain gemstones is split into the colours of the rainbow; and 'brilliance', the return of light to the eye from within the gemstone (hence why it is also known as 'internal lustre').

Everyone who collects gemstones will have their own views about what attracts them to certain coloured stones and not to others; I for one can't always put my finger on why I love certain gems in my collection more than others.

However, a mixture of a gem's colour, clarity and cut are normally the main reasons, even if the conscious mind does not necessarily realise it. These three elements also play a major role in the amount of brilliance seen in a gemstone.

When the colour of a gemstone is more vivid, its brilliance will normally not be as high. For example, you will see more brilliance in a Sky Blue Topaz than in a London Blue Topaz. The better the clarity, the fewer obstructions light has

to negotiate in order to enter and exit the gem, the more likely you are to see a higher level of brilliance.

Most important of all is the quality cut of the gem: if the angles of the facets are poorly applied, the gem will not come to life!

Whilst a Diamond is cut to display a mixture of brilliance, dispersion and scintillation at their best, the key priority when shaping a coloured gemstone is how to best display the gem's colour; and in the case of transparent gems how to also maximise the gem's brilliance. The most important factor in the cut is the angle of the pavilion facets; in simple terms, the facets on the underside of the gem act like mirrors on which light is refracted. However, don't expect all gemstones to have the same proportions and angles of that familiar picture of a Diamond, as different gemstones have different optimal angles for the return of light (known as a gemstone's 'critical angle').

The best way to see brilliance is to hold the gem so that your light source is hitting the facets on the crown and then slowly move it from side to side in a rocking motion. What you should

see are patches of light within the gem. If you can't see any brilliance, then the gem is opaque (not transparent), heavily included, too dark in tone or poorly cut.

The colour seen by the eye from the lustre of a gemstone is known as its "key colour", whilst the colour seen as a result of the gem's brilliance is known as its key colour. This key colour is often assumed to be white, but on closer inspection, although lighter than the body colour of the gem, you will normally notice that it is in fact a coloured sparkle and not a white one.

Peridot is one of the most brilliant gems on the planet.

Brilliant Cut

If you see triangle and kite shaped facets on a gem, it is a brilliant cut stone.

The "Brilliant Cut" or round cut is the most popular cut for Diamonds and is often used for transparent coloured gemstones as it is an ideal shape for maximising the light returned through the top of a gem.

The brilliant cut we know today has been developed throughout recent history by a number of cutters. It was first introduced in the mid 17th Century and at that stage featured 17 facets on the crown. A Venetian polisher called Vincent Peruzzi increased the number of facets to 33 and by the end of the 17th century, the Lisbon cut and Brazilian cut featured 58 facets, giving rise to a dramatic increase in the gem's beauty through greater dispersion and higher brilliance.

In 1919, Marcel Tolkowsky studied the round brilliant cut and detailed geometric calculations to further improve the cut. He specified the exact angles of the facets and the percentage of the gem that should be above and below the girdle in order to maximise

the brilliance and fire seen in a Diamond. Even today, almost 90 years later, Tolkowsky's calculations are still adhered to by most Lapidarists when cutting round brilliant cut Diamonds.

The modern round brilliant cut consists of 57 facets (sometimes 58 if at the point where the pavilions meet, a small facet is added running parallel to the crown). There are 33 facets cut on the crown and 25 on the pavilion.

Please note that the brilliant cut is not exclusively used on round gemstones and if you see an oval, trilliant etc, where the facets appear to be a mix of triangles and kite shapes, then that is a brilliant cut.

In fact nearly all cut gemstones fall into one of just four main categories: either they are fancy cut (no pre-defined arrangement of facets), cabochon cut, step cut or brilliant cut. It is important not to confuse a gem's cut with a gem's shape. A heart shaped gemstone is exactly that, a heart shaped gem stone; the cut of a heart shape is normally a brilliant cut.

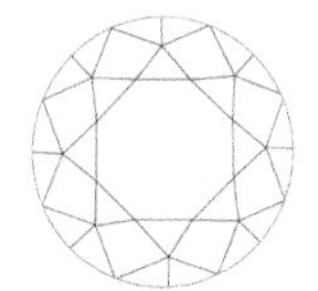

Bronze Age Jewellery

Gemstones such as Jet and Amber were frequently used in Bronze Age jewellery.

The Bronze Age can be split into three periods; Early Bronze Age (3500-2200 BC), Middle Bronze Age (2200-1550 BC), and Late Bronze Age (1550-1200 BC).

Metalsmiths in the Bronze Age developed an astonishingly high level of skill in bronze and gold working and used twisting and forging methods to make wrist and neck torques.

Towards the final stages of the Early Bronze Age and the start of the Middle Bronze Age, a new type of jewellery appeared in the Budapest region. This new jewellery included rings which were not complete bands as they are today, but instead had twisted ends. Other types of jewellery included spiral necklaces, and corkscrew and half-moon styled earrings. The spread of jewellery along the Danube area helps confirm the formation of the trade route of the Early Bronze Age. From this jewellery, mostly found in Bronze Age graves, it has been possible to reconstruct what was fashionable in the Middle Bronze Age.

In 2005 a discovery of a shipwreck off the coast of Salcombe in Devon shed new light on Britain's overseas ancient trade. Whilst the ship itself had rotted, gold and bronze jewellery was discovered in excellent condition.

Burma The most famous source of ruby on the planet.

Due to Burma's recent political instability and trade embargoes placed on the country, some of the world's finest Sapphires, Rubies and Spinels are not available in some countries such as America.

Although some gems have funded conflict (especially Jade which has been mined under military rule and therefore Burmese Jade should be totally avoided), many of the gems being smuggled out of the country along its border with Thailand are by small artisanal miners, who are selling

the gems to support their families during the country's instability. The world's finest Rubies come from Burma and with all the country's recent traumas, with military rule and cyclones, if you can be sure of how the gems were mined and can trust your sources, and you can be sure some of your cash ends up directly in the pocket of those that need it most, then it surely adds even more beauty to the gems you acquire. However, at GemsTV and RocksTV we always operate within the laws of the countries where we sell our jewellery.

Although there are several areas in Burma where gems are unearthed, the most famous gem region in the country and possibly in the entire world is the Mogok Valley.
Known by many in the trade as the "Valley of Rubies", it is without doubt the most important source of Rubies in the world.

The valley stretches for some twenty miles and at its widest point it exceeds two miles. The Rubies from this area are world renowned for their truly deep, intense red colour. They lack the presence of iron found in Rubies from other locations and this leads to a stronger fluorescence and an extremely vivid saturation.

The next most significant source of fine Rubies in Burma is Mong Hsu; this region lies between the Mogok Valley and the border with Thailand. Rubies discovered here tend to feature a hue that is a purplish red.

Although not as famous as its Rubies, Burma is also the source of some of the world's finest Sapphires, although unfortunately supply is incredibly limited. These tend to be of a very dark, intense, pure colour and are often referred to as "Royal Blue". They normally have a hue of around 80 to 85% blue, with the remainder being made up of purple. Compared to Kashmir (the other benchmark for Sapphires), Burmese Sapphires have better transparency. For me the perfect Sapphire would be one that has the openness of colour of a Kashmir, combined with the diaphaneity of a Burmese Sapphire.

Similar to most gem mining communities, there is very little technology or mechanisation involved in the industry, with most of the mining taking place in alluvial deposits, using buckets, spades and sieves.

ANNA BELLA
BIJOU DE MER
Boutique
COLLECTION
Eduardina
RENO
GEM COLLECTOR
jessica lili
Jaipurium
KAMA CHARMS
LORIQUE
MATTOM
MILANO CHARMS
MUSICLOVER
SARAH BENNETT
GEMSTONE
JEWELLERY
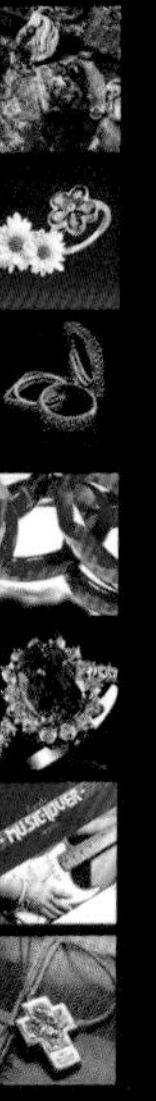

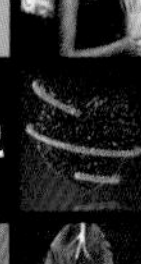

The Little Book of Gemstones (B)
www.tggc.com

All enquiries should be directed to:
The Genuine Gemstone Company Limited, Unit 2D
Eagle Road, Moons Moat
Redditch, Worcestershire, B98 9HF

ISBN: 978-0-9559972-4-2
Published by The Genuine Gemstone Company Limited
Designed by The Genuine Gemstone Company Limited

We constantly travel the globe to discover new gemstones.
Scan this QR code on a mobile device to read the latest news.